Down Our Street

Alice said he couldn't
And Adam said he wouldn't
And Ulie said he shouldn't
But Jason DID.
He let his mouse run free
On the classroom floor.
You've never heard such nattering
                    such clattering
                    such shattering
As when that mouse ran free
On the classroom floor . . .

JENNIFER & GRAEME CURRY

Down Our Street

Illustrated by Scoular Anderson

A Magnet Book

First published in Great Britain 1988
by Methuen Children's Books Ltd
This Magnet paperback edition first published 1989
by Methuen Children's Books
A Division of the Octopus Publishing Group Ltd
Michelin House, 81 Fulham Road, London SW3 6RB
Text copyright © 1988 Jennifer & Graeme Curry
Illustrations copyright © 1988 Scoular Anderson
Printed in Great Britain
by Cox & Wyman Ltd, Reading

ISBN 0 416 06472 8

For Laura

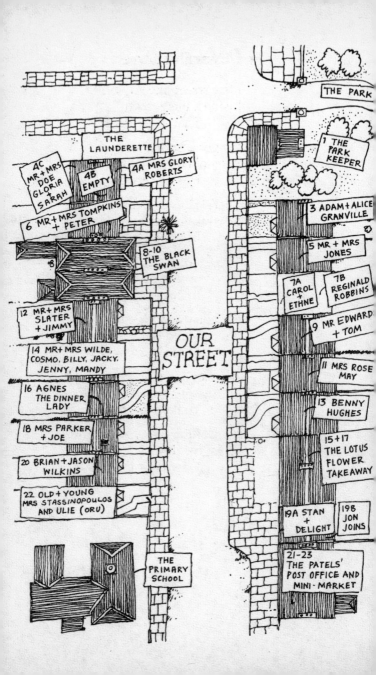

Down Our Street

It's a street like any other
Inside a busy town . . .
     That's our street.

It's got a park at one end,
A school down by the other . . .
     Has our street.

There's lots of people in it,
In houses, flats and shops . . .
     In our street.

There's dogs and cats in plenty,
A parrot and a mouse . . .
     In our street.

It's noisy and it's dirty,
It's crowded but it's fun . . .
     That's our street.

A street like any other –
But the one that we call home . . .
     That's our street.

It's waiting with a welcome,
So follow us and come . . .
     Down our street.

The Game

It was the football that started it.
Jason took a kick at it
And kicked poor Ulie's knee instead.
Ulie yelled, his arm shot up,
And Jimmy got it, in the neck.
Jimmy saw red, he charged like a bull,
Butted his head into Adam's chest.
Alice shouted, 'That's a foul,'
Grabbed the ball and threw it hard.
Peter caught it, on his nose.
'I'll bleed to death,' he screamed aloud.
Joey saw the funny side,
Got a bucket, ran like mad,
Stumbled, slipped, then fell full length,
And *roared*. Out the grown-ups came.

'You hooligan crew,' said Mr Patel,
'The street's not safe with the likes of you.
Flipping kids . . . nothing but noise . . .
Why don't you go elsewhere to play?'

They pick themselves up and shake themselves
  down
Wipe their noses and smooth their hair,
Grumble their way to the pitch in the park.
'Not fair!' mumbles Jason. 'Life's not fair!'

Alice at the Cricket Match

Down the park
Just before sunset
Our brother's batting
And although he's good,
Oh yes, he's very good,
When he's out
He won't go.

'Howzat!' shouts Brian
When the ball hits our brother on the pad.
'A mile off,' says our brother,
'Anyone could see that.'

'Howzat!' screams Sarah
As she takes an easy catch.
'No ball,' says our brother,
'Anyone could see that.'

'Howzat!' I say
As the stumps shatter.
'I wasn't ready,' says our brother,
'OK, I'm ready now.'

And at the end of the game
When the sun's gone down
And our brother stands undefeated
On 146,
He says,
'See you all tomorrow,
Same time, same place,
And remember –
I'm still not out!'

The Pond Froze

In January the pond froze.
At first, just flakes of ice
Floating on the water.
Then, they joined up,
Got bigger, and bigger.
At last the pond was covered
And the ice was strong enough
To hold a weight.

Terrier Tom was the first
To go on it.
Slithering and slipping,
Lifting his leg
When he got right across
As if to show
He wasn't bothered.

Then Billy Wilde.
'Come back, our Tom.'
But the dog didn't,
So he followed him instead.
And their Jacky
Followed Billy,
The way he always did.

And then, all us street kids
Were on the pond,
Sliding and skating,
Shouting and falling.
And laughing. Laughing
As if we'd burst.

'Get back here,'
The grown-ups yelled.
'Come on off. You'll all
Fall in. You'll drown.
The ice will break.'

But the ice held.
We played there
Till after dark.
Till long after
The street lights
Were shining
In the black.

That was a good day.
That was one of
The best days
Ever.

The New Thing in the Park

It's got a sort of
steel spring at
the bottom of it,
with bounces built right into it,
silvery and strong.

It's got a sort of
bucket thing on
the top of it,
with a seat down there inside of it,
shiny and red.

It's got a sort of
foot-hold in
the front of it,
and handles all around of it,
clingy and safe.

It makes you sort of
giggle, then you
wriggle, and you
splutter and you
squeak.

It makes you sort of
fizzy, then you're
dizzy, then you're
spun round till you're
weak.

WHAT IS IT?   It's the sort of
                     new thing in
                     the playground in
                     the corner of the
park.

Graffiti

JESUS SAVES – BUT LINEKER SCORES ON THE
  REBOUND
'I like that one,'
Says the man from the Council,
At the top of his ladder
With his paint and his brush.

NOTHING SUCCEEDS LIKE A BUDGIE
He's at the park-keeper's house
At the end of the terrace,
Slapping on paint
From his tin of whitewash.

I DON'T THINK CRAZY PAVING'S ALL IT'S
  CRACKED UP TO BE
'I like that one too,'
Says the man from the Council
And covers it up
With a sweep of his brush.

GRAFFITI'S DAYS ARE NUMBERED – THE
  WRITING'S ON THE WALL
He comes every month,
The man from the Council,
At the top of his ladder
With his paint and his brush.

The Park Keeper

Eight in the morning
When I'm making my tea,
They stream past my hut
Waving sadly at me –
Joggers!
Have you ever seen a happy one?

Just after one
And the litter shows up:
Wrappings and fag ends
And the odd paper cup –
Office workers!
Show me a tidy one!

Four o'clock sharp
And the children descend
With their games and their fights,
Drives me clean round the bend –
Kids!
Have you ever come across a quiet one?

But my favourite time's
When the sun's going down
Just before closing
When I'm all on my own –
Dusk,
Just me and the park.

Green

Sitting in the launderette
Delight and Carol, side by side,
Watch their washing whirl around,
Wishing it was done and dried.

Delight begins to paint her nails
While Carol sits and stares.
First vivid green, then silver specks,
To match the shoes she wears.

Then Carol says, 'That Stan of yours,
He's quite a guy, you know.
We met him down the Rink last week –
That day you didn't go.

He really fancies Eth, he does,
Don't say you hadn't heard.'
Delight begins to paint her toes,
She doesn't say a word.

'I think he asked her for a date –
Of course, I couldn't swear –
He never took his eyes off her,
That day that you weren't there.'

Delight gets slowly to her feet,
Walks up to Carol's machine,
Tips the paint in the top of it,
And watches her washing turn green.

A Sleepy Saturday

Mrs Parker's washing her car.
Mrs Jones gives her dog a shout.
But apart from that, all is still,
There are no men about.

'It's like the war,' says Glory Roberts,
'When they all went off to fight.
Those were strange days for all of us
When there wasn't a man in sight.'

But just then the men come out of their homes,
Laughing, enjoying the sun.
The game is over, the TV's switched off,
The FA Cup Final is won.

Twins Going Home from School

In Alice's head
There are
Ballet shoes
And 'Top of the Pops',
A pair of faded blue jeans,
The school's baby rabbit –
Called Tosh –
And the doughnut she's taking home for tea.

In Adam's pocket
There are
Rubber bands
And plasticine,
An empty packet of vinegar crisps,
His old dirty hanky –
With a hole –
And the doughnut he's taking home for tea.

Old Mrs Glory Roberts

Old Mrs Glory Roberts
Lives all alone except for her cats.
Her house was once
The best and the biggest,
But now it's all been turned into flats.

Old Mrs Glory Roberts
Waters her herbs in their earthenware pot.
Her garden was once
A flourishing acre,
But now it's only a cat-prowled plot.

Old Mrs Glory Roberts
Sits and laughs in the morning sun,
Calls to her sleek
Soft-stepping companions,
Greets them by name as they come every one.

'Come Sheba and Shaftoe and Selim and Sue,
Millicent, Moggy and Mo,
Now Barney and Benny, with one-eared Bee,
And my own little cross-eyed Beau.
Come Felix, Fenella and Freddy and Flops,
And Maurice, the one with no tail,
Then Jingo and Jackie and gentle old Joe,
Who's fourteen, and getting quite frail.'

Old Mrs Glory Roberts
Sits with her friends in the midday glare,
And the air is loud
With the purring they make,
And the milky content that she shares with
    them there.

Room to Let

There's nobody living in No. 4b.
They've packed up and gone to Torbay.
Their flat is to let,
So who will we get,
Squeezed in there between c and a?

Mum read in the newspaper, just last night
– the column called *Bedsits to Let* –
'Spac. rm., K & B,
C.H. & S/C,'
And Dad said, 'That's it, what d'you bet?'

There's kids up above there, and cats down below,
No garden, and too many stairs,
But *someone* will come
In search of a home,
And be glad for 4b to be theirs.

The Hero of Dead-Eye Gorge

When Mrs Doe took Gloria
To the library – to change her books –
The balloon went too,
Floating, blue and beautiful,
Above the pushchair.

'There's a lovely balloon!'
Said Jon Joins, looking up from the shelf
Where the Cowboys and Westerns stayed.
Gloria gurgled, and gave it to him
With her fat little hand.
'Oh no,' he said. 'It's yours,'
And handed it back.

But –

The balloon escaped,
Flew up and up
And stuck on the ceiling.

Jon grabbed a chair,
Leapt up on it as if it were
A runaway stallion,
Balanced, and stretched –
And couldn't reach.
Gloria opened her mouth to howl.

'Really!' snapped Mrs Jones,
Slamming down the book,
My Life with the Royal Family,
'Libraries are supposed to be *quiet*!'

But now Jon Joins was John Wayne,
Cowboy of cowboys,
And he had ridden into town
To help a dame in distress.

'Leave it to me, lady,' said Jon,
As he moseyed round the room.
Then he tossed the chair
On a table,
Vaulted on top,
Grabbed the balloon –
And saved the day.

Gloria giggled.
Mrs Doe smiled.
Jon beamed,
And swaggered away
Magnificently,
Like the hero
Of Dead-Eye Gorge.

Mrs Jones stared at a picture
Of the Royal Corgis.
'I thought libraries were supposed
To be *quiet!*' she muttered.

'SHUSH!' hissed the librarian.

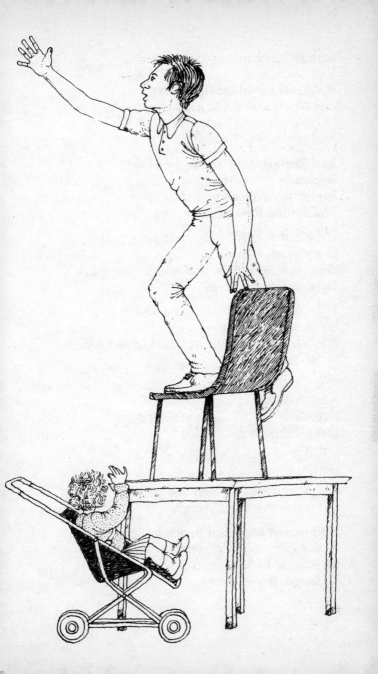

Street Party

It's Royal Wedding Day today,
The whole street's in a state.
There's coke and crisps for all of us,
And white cake on a plate.

They'd chosen Sarah for the bride,
Dressed up in curtain lace,
And Brian Wilkins was the groom –
You should have seen his face!

They had to drive right round the park
In a sort of open car,
Till Sarah went pale, and *nearly* was sick,
Though it wasn't really far.

Then Brian had to give her a kiss
Right up there on the stage,
But she yelled, 'NO!' and ducked her head . . .
So he thumped her in a rage.

The grown-ups laughed, and clapped their hands,
And said, 'Oh, look at that!'
But Sarah's mum was not amused.
She hit Brian with her hat.

Reginald Robbins has a stall
With things for us to buy –
Mugs, and spoons, and badges too,
But the prices are sky-high.

And now it's time for dancing
With lights up in the trees.
Mr Joins asks Mrs Jones
To tango, if you please.

And Rose May wears a cardboard crown
Of blue and gold and red.
The nurse gives her a warning look,
But she will not go to bed.

There's noise, and mess, and barking dogs –
It really is a treat.
It's Royal Wedding Day today . . .
Especially down our street.

The Day of the Gulls

On a silver-cold day
Under snow-heavy clouds
The seagulls come
Driven inland
Swooping and screaming
Over the scraps in the gutters.

The children stare
As the street is made beautiful
By the white shining
Of their wings.

The New Car at No. 5

They've just got a new car down our street,
The Jones, at No. 5.
It's a *new* new car, not second-hand,
And Mrs J's learning to drive.
Mum says they must have won the Pools
Or backed a winning horse.
Dad says they're throwing good money away –
He's jealous though, of course.

It's a *new* new car, not second-hand,
Pale blue, with a silvery shine.
'Metallic finish', that's what it's called –
I wish that it was mine!
We all lined up to sit inside,
Pete Tompkins, Joe and me.
'You must be joking!' Mrs J said,
'Just look at the state of you three,

Your hands are black as black can be,
Your shoes are filthy too,
There's grease all over the seats of your pants –
It's not for the likes of you!'

It's a *new* new car, not second-hand,
Too smart for kids like us.
It looks all right, I'll grant you that,
But I reckon we'll go by bus.

Coal Black – Grass Green

There's a tree grows in the street,
Only one, as if it's an accident,
Thrusting out of the paving stones
Beside the kerb outside the Tompkins' house.
Pete's tree.
A laburnum, it's called.
In the spring it turns to green and gold
With leaves and blossom,
But in the winter, it's black.
Coal black.

One chilly day Pete went
Into the country
For a day out
With his dad,
And there were laburnums there,
But not the same.
Their trunks were green.
Grass green.

Peter shook his head.
'Laburnums are black,' he said.
But his father laughed.
'Only in towns. It's the cars, you see.
Their fumes and filth,
They make them black.
Coal black.'

When Peter got home
He fetched a bucket
Of soap and water
And a hard-bristled brush.
And he scrubbed. And he scrubbed.
Then he smiled.
'My laburnum's green,' he said.
'Grass green.'

The Break-In

The girls come giggling round the corner
Hurrying home from the disco dance.
Twelve o'clock – that's midnight striking.
The street is sleeping, dark and still.

'Find your key,' says Ethne, shivering,
'I haven't got mine, so look for yours.'
Carol searches, hunts all over,
Handbag, pockets in all her clothes.

'I think it's lost,' she says to Ethne,
'I can't find it anywhere.
What'll we do? The house is locked.
We never thought to hide a spare.'

They try the windows, no luck there,
Securely bolted, every one.
They think of ringing Reg's doorbell,
But he'll go mad, so they don't dare.

'Nothing for it,' Carol says,
'We'll have to break in best we can,
We'll smash a little windowpane,
You crawl through, and let me in.'

Ethne fumes, 'My tights will split,
And my best skirt – it's hardly the thing!'
But she breaks the glass and puts her hand through,
Slides back the bolt, and scrambles in.

Just halfway through – and here's a car,
With flashing lights, and siren too.
'Now then, now then, what's this about?
We're the police. A word with you.

Perhaps you'd tell us what you're doing,
What you're up to, who you are.
Maybe you'd better come to the Station.
This way, ladies, into the car.'

Later, when the fuss is over,
Tucked in their beds at the end of the day,
There's only one question that hasn't been
    answered –
Who called the cops out to Flat 7a?

Reginald Robbins

I'm Reginald Robbins, a military man.
Retired now, of course, but I'm still spick and span.
My tiepin is straight and my shoes always shine.
I'm a military man, and I stay in line.

I'll show you some photos, you'll get the idea.
Those are my boys, the platoon in Algiers.
There's Taffy and Roger and Jumbo and Jock,
The best in the world, the pick of the crop.

No, I never married, I didn't have time.
My life was the army, the desert, the Rhine.
A good bunch of chaps, we still stay in touch,
And we meet once a year, up in town, for lunch.

Yes, I'm on my own now, but I keep myself fit,
A walk every morning, I play golf a bit.
Oh, I missed having children, I'm sure you can tell,
But I served my country, and I served it well.

Pedro

Pedro, the ice cream man,
Drives down our street
In his ice cream van.
And he brings:
    Barmybananapeanutcrunch
    Colaquenchandchococream
    Orangecoolermintymunch
    Ninetyninesandpineappledream.

Pedro, the ice cream seller,
Works every night
For his friend, Bertorella.
And he cooks:
    Hamburgersandhotdogs
    Freshfriedfishandjuicysteaks
    Jamdoughnutsandapplepie
    Sugaredwaffleshotpancakes.

Ambition

When Tom was five, he wanted to be . . .
    an engine driver.
When Tom was six, he wanted to be . . .
    a football player.
When Tom was seven, he wanted to be . . .
    a circus trainer.
When Tom was eight, he wanted to be . . .
    a deep-sea diver.
When Tom was nine, he wanted to be . . .
    an aquarium keeper.
Today Tom's ten. He doesn't want to be . . .
    out of work –
    like his dad.

Tom's Party

Ulie was sick
'Cos Jason
Put salt
On the jelly.
Little Jenny
Wet her knickers
And wanted
To go home.
Jimmy Slater
Burst the balloons –
All twenty of them.
And the cat sat
On the cake.
Adam punched Sarah
Because she called Alice
'A stuck-up thing'.
And Billy Wilde
Said the video
Was 'Bor-*ing*!'
It was a pretty
Ordinary sort of
Party really –
The day that
Tom was ten.

BAR

The Black Swan

When it's full
It's noisy
It's smoky
It's bustling
It's fun
And there's
No room
To move
In the bar of the Swan.

When it's empty
It's quiet
It's sad
It's dirty
It's stale
And a
Lonely
Old man
Sups the Black Swan's ale.

Rose May and Hollyhock High

Hollyhocks grow in Rose May's garden
Hollyhock-bright and hollyhock-high

She counts them
One by one
As she lifts her frame
Carefully
Painfully
Over the broken pavings
With the grass jutting through
To the loo
At the end of the path.

Hollyhocks grow in Rose May's garden
Hollyhock-bright and hollyhock-high

She used to think
They reached to the sky
When she was little
Happily
Joyfully
Skipping and jumping
Doing her handstands
On the grass
At the edge of the wall.

Hollyhocks grow in Rose May's garden
Hollyhock-bright and hollyhock-high

She sees them
From her window

As she tugs on her frock
Achingly
Awkwardly
For the nurse who says
'You must get up,
Get dressed, get about,
Don't give in, never say die.'

Hollyhocks grow in Rose May's garden
Hollyhock-bright and hollyhock-high

But when she cries
They bend their heads
And their petals drop
. . . Like tears.

Jon Joins

Jon Joins is
A joiner.

'What's a joiner?'
I ask my dad.

'A joiner
Is a bloke
Who joins
This and that,'
He says.
'Or
That and this.'

'So is Jon Joins
Called Jon Joins
Because he joins
This and that?'
I ask.
'*Or*
That and this?'

'Course not!'
Says my dad.
'Jon Joins
Would be called
Jon Joins . . .
Even
If he didn't.'

Street Cats

In the summer
The street cats
Bask on the roofs
Pretending to be
Lions in the Serengeti.

Pigeons

They're only pigeons
The grafters of the air,
Carving a living out of
Turned-over dustbins
And Rose May's breadcrumbs.

City Bees

In a drab back yard
At the back of the shop
Among boxes and bins
A world away
From flowering fields
And hedgerows in blossom
Mr Patel keeps bees.

City bees.
They browse on buddleia and
Ragged weeds
Rosebay willowherb
And dust-heavy trees
But their busy wings
Bring sweetness
To the city.

First Snow

And then the snow came,
Quiet and still in the night,
Smudging the houses,
The shops and the school,
Veiling the park
In its frosted lace.

Little Gloria looked from
Her window and laughed –
Then cried,
Not knowing why.

Shoes

Jack Slater's
Under his car again
Feet sticking out
Brown shoes
Grey socks

'What's up, Jack?' says Benny
'Gasket's past it,' say the shoes

Jack Slater and Benny Hughes
Both under the car
Feet sticking out
Brown shoes
Grey socks
Red trainers
Green socks

'What's up, Jack?' says Stan
'Exhaust's exhausted,' say the shoes

Jack Slater, Benny Hughes and Stan the Biker
All under the car
Feet sticking out
Brown shoes
Grey socks
Red trainers
Green socks
Winklepickers
Black socks

'What's up, Jack?' says Mr Wilde
'Carburettor could be better,' say the shoes

So Mr Wilde gives the car a kick
Not a gentle tap
A full-blooded kick
And the engine bursts into life
Purring like a well-fed cat

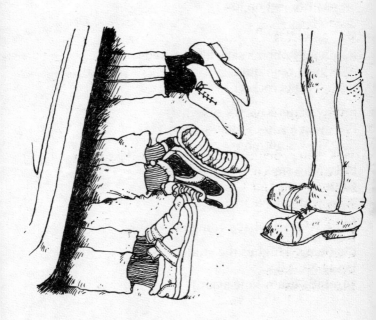

The Middle of the Night

When it's dark down our street
There's always one light shining
(A desk lamp, not very bright)

When it's quiet down our street
There's always music playing
(Elvis Costello, mostly)

When it's cold down our street
There's always one fire burning
(A gas fire, set on low)

What's going on?

Reginald Robbins says it's the Reds
Plotting a revolution
(He's off his rocker)

Jimmy Slater says it's scientists
Planning a trip to Mars
(He knows nothing)

Rose May says it's Santa Claus
Getting ready for Christmas
(Can you believe it?)

But we know what's going on

It's Benny Hughes the student
Up at No.13
(And it's exam-time again)

Wilde By Name . . .

Cosmo's weird and Billy's naughty,
Jacky's odd and Jenny's rude,
Baby Mandy's just plain dirty –
They're a terrible lot, that wild Wilde brood.

Their dad won't work, he goes to the boozer,
Or hammers away out there in his shed.
Their mum won't cook, she goes to the chippy,
And when she wants to, stays in bed.

Their neighbours say that they're disgraceful,
They'd report them, if they dare.
The funny thing is – they seem quite happy.
I sometimes wish that I lived there.

Mr Wilde and His Teapots

Mrs Jones says my dad is
'An out-of-work yobbo'.
But my dad says
He's an artist.

My dad makes teapots.
My dad's a teapot freak.
He makes 'em out of tin,
From tin cans, and that.
He has a special tool
To cut the tin, and flatten it.
And then he turns it
And bends it and fashions it.
And he makes it into teapots.

Not ordinary teapots, of course.
Special ones. Like machines,
And cars, and petrol pumps, and that.
The best one he made
Was like the engine of a train.
It had a tender behind – for sugar –
And it pulled six oil drums.
And each oil drum – that was a cup.

My dad's an artist, he is.
My dad's an artist in teapots.

Cosmo's Parrot

Cosmo Wilde brought home
A parrot.
He found it in a phone box,
He said.
He called it Russell, after the
Phone box,
Which was in Russell Street.
Green, red
And orange it was – the parrot,
I mean,
Not the phone box, of course.
The parrot
Loved Mrs Wilde and hated
Her husband.
Every day it tried
To peck
Little holes all over
Mr Wilde.
But try as it might, it
Could not.
Its beak was too blunt.

Today
Mrs Wilde has bought a
Sharpening stone,
To put in Russell's cage!

Mouse Up a Tree

Every Sunday
Jenny climbs
Her own special tree
In the park.

One Sunday,
Halfway up,
She sees someone else
Up there.

'Hello,' says Joe.
'D'you think you'd like
To hold my mouse
For me?

She's called Snow White –
A cissy name –
But she's not bad,
You know.'

The mouse sits quiet,
Heaving gently
In Jenny's hands.
'I'm off,'

Says Joe. 'My dinner's cooked.
Just you hang on
And I'll be back,
OK?

My mum don't like
A mouse in the house,
But I'm working on it,
See?'

By tea-time Jenny's
Had enough
And scrambles down
The tree.

She knocks on the door
Of the Parkers' house.
'I've brought the mouse,
For Joe.'

Mrs Parker peers
Then turns quite pale.
'Oh no you don't!'
She says.

'I've just made Joe
Get rid of his –
We don't want one
Of yours.'

Street Dogs

Terrier Tom lives at No.14,
    Only one eye and a stump of a tail.
Roars down our street like a bad-tempered wind,
    Dines on pork pie and a saucer of ale.

Cherry Pie Champ is the pride of the Jones',
    Gleaming white coat and a collar of blue.
Stares from the window at old Glory's cats,
    Pampered and bored, with nothing to do.

Scamp's called 'the happy dog', fat and content,
    Lies on the park wall, basks in the sun,
Sits by the lamp-post and *smiles* all the day.
    Never moves far from his home, No.1.

But Wilfred's our school dog, as brown as a wolf,
    Rough-haired and lanky, with eyes glinting green.
Begs for Maltesers, cheese sarnies and crisps,
    'Stands up' for Jesus, 'dies' for the Queen.

Lotus Flower Takeaway

Number one
Egg Foo Yung
Number two
Chicken with Bamboo
Number three
Shrimp Chop Suey
Number four
Rice galore
Number five
Forget your knife
Number six
Chopsticks
Number seven
Mmm, this is heaven
Number eight
Forget your weight
Number nine
Hands off, that's mine
Number ten
Same again!

Night Prowler

Skulking round the dustbins,
Flame-red in dead of night,
Sharp-pricked ears, dark plume of a tail –
Urban fox on the back street trail.

Letter to Cissie

'Thanking you for yours of the 14th,
With all its news and that.
Who'd have believed it
About your boy, Ronnie?
You must be that proud.
The weather here is terrible,
Raining cats and dogs.
Running down the gutters in buckets.
Wet! The kids is like drowned rats.
Soaked to the skin, just like drowned rats . . .'

> On Tuesdays, Agnes the Dinner Lady
> Writes a letter to her friend, Cissie,
> Who's moved far away from our Street
> To live in the sun in Majorca,
> So as to be near to her son, Ronald.

'. . . You remember old Rosie May?
Real poorly she is, poor thing,
With those rheumatics of hers.
Can't hardly get out of bed.
It's the damp that does it, nurse says.
Makes the aches worse.
But Mrs Parker's Joe, he's a good lad.
He sees her right. Does her shopping.
Chats her up. Buys her bull's-eyes. Makes her tea
And crumpets, with the butter dripping
   through . . .'

Each Tuesday, the letter is longer than the
    last.
Each Tuesday, when dinners are done,
Agnes racks her brains
For more and more news.
News for her old friend, Cissie.

'. . . That Mrs Jones, down the end,
She's as stuck up as ever she was.
Gave me a right mouthful, she did,
Just for giving her dog a biscuit.
Cherry Pie Champ? More like Skin and Bone.
More like a little skinned rabbit. "Oh please,"
    she says,
In that silly whine of hers, "Oh *please*!
Biscuits is so *bad* for him!"
"Pardon me for living," says I! . . .'

    Agnes counts the pages,
    Frowns and chews her pen,
    Screws up her face and racks her brains,
    There must be more to tell –
    More, more, *more* to tell.

'Them kids'll be the death of me
One day, you mark my words.
Last week that Jason found a worm
Crawling in the mud, the dirty thing,
And put it in my nice clean mash.
Scream! Blue murder, I screamed!
"Why d'you want to go and do a thing like that?"
    says I.
"Poor little worm," says he, as if butter wouldn't
    melt.

"Worms get hungry too, ain't you got no heart?"
Heart? I'll give him heart. Feel my hand, more like.'

Agnes smiles, and stretches.
Nods, puts down her pen.
21 pages of news from the Street.
Cissie managed just 19.
This week, this week, *this* week she's won.

The Postman

'I don't deliver letters,'
Says our postman,
'I deliver emotions.

Take this morning.

Happiness for Jason –
He's been asked for a trial
For the local schools' football team.

Sadness for Glory Roberts –
A cousin has died peacefully
In his sleep.

Boredom for Benny –
Another special offer
Cut-price double glazing.

Anger for Mr Wilde –
A gas bill
He just can't believe.

Love for Ethne –
A Valentine
On an autumn day.

They look like letters,'
Says our postman,
'But it's a sackful of emotions.'

Joe Parker and Election Fever

I was on my way to the mini-market
Down our street
To get a loaf of bread
When this man with a megaphone
Shouts something in my ear
And pats me on the head,
A great fat man
In a baggy suit
With a red carnation in his lapel.

I buy the bread and on my way home
This lady gives me a badge
And kisses me on the cheek,
A fat grey-haired lady
Wearing a smart blue dress
With a blue carnation in her lapel.

When I got home,
Sweating,
I told my mum and she said,
'Don't worry
It's only the election.
They've gone now
And they won't be back
For five years.'

The Slalom

On one of those bright, chilly autumn days
Mrs Parker,
Driving home from work in her Renault,
Bumped Jack Slater's Sierra with her mudguard –
At least he said she did.
'Oh no I didn't,' said Mrs Parker
And so on.

Until Jack Slater said,
'Pah! Women drivers!'
'We'll soon see who's the better driver!'
Said Mrs Parker
And she issued her challenge.

We all turned out the next day
Wrapped up in scarves and woolly hats.
Reginald Robbins, the referee,
Laid out the course –
Six shining cones,
The sort roadworkers use.
(Stan the Biker found them,
But he wouldn't say where.)

Mrs Parker went first.
It was a joy to watch
As she eased the Renault
Gracefully through the course,
Executed a faultless three-point turn
And glided back to the start.
We all cheered, of course
(Especially the women).

Thinking about it later
We decided Jack Slater
Tried to go too fast.
He skidded and slid,
Bumped and thumped,
And knocked over all the cones
(As well as our dustbin).

Poor Jack Slater

But that's what happens
If you try to take on
The driver of the No. 9 bus.

The No.9 Bus

The No.9 bus is the best bus in town
And that suits our street fine
It comes every ten minutes
Though not on the dot
That's the No.9.

The No.9 bus is a good-looking bus
Flaunting its shimmer and shine
Red and silver
Bold and brassy
That's the No.9.

The No.9 bus is a racing bus
First past the winning line
Roaring past motorbikes
Overtaking sports cars
That's the No.9.

The No.9 is a detective bus
First to the scene of the crime
Mean and moody
Prowling the streets
That's the No.9.

The No.9 is a scruffy bus
Covered with dirt and with slime
At the end of the day
It's earned its pay
That's the No.9.

Stan the Biker

Stan the Biker rides a Honda,
Huge and dirty – 500 cc –
But when he thunders down our street
Muddy heels are all you see,
Heels on wheels.

Stan the Biker and his girlfriend,
A leather-clad moll by the name of Delight,
Do wheelies and wobblies and screeches and slides
And wake up the neighbours all through the night,
Squeals on wheels.

In the winter Stan the Biker
Loads up his Honda with meat and two veg.
He rides up the street and visits the old folk,
Glory and Rose and, of course, Reg,
Meals on wheels.

The Noise

One dark night, in the rain and the sleet,
A strange, strange noise was heard down our street,
Of rattling and shaking and shouting and yells,
Of clashing and crashing, of cymbals and bells.

The dogs laid low and the birds took fright,
Old Glory Roberts shut out the night.
Doors were locked and windows bolted,
But still the sound rattled and jarred and jolted.

In the Black Swan they pulled down the shutters.
Reg said, 'I thought we were rid of those nutters.'
But the decibels grew and the noise got worse,
As Stan's heavy metal band tried to rehearse.

Toenails

'Any old toenails today, Mr Joins?'
        'You what?'
'Old toenails.'
        'Get off!'

Jon Joins shoulders
His bag of tools
And strides off down the street.
Close on his heels,
Determined shadow,
Jacky Wilde follows.

'I'm collecting.'
        'Collecting what?'
'Toenails, of course.'
        'You're nuts!'

All in separate
Cardboard boxes,
Each one labelled
With name and date.
All done properly,
Neatly ordered,
Toenail collecting's
The latest rage.

'Go on, Mr Joins.
Be a hero, Jon.'
        Jon Joins shrugs.
        'Call round Friday,' he says,
        'Friday's toenails, son.'

Tennis

In summer when the sun is hot
And flies and bugs are a menace,
Brian and Joe get their racquets and ball
And set up the net for tennis.

The net is an old length of washing-line
And the lawn is their Centre Court,
But Becker v Lendl, Brian v Joe,
The battle is just as hard fought.

The first set is Brian's, the second is Joe's,
Everything rests on the third,
But the sun goes down when they're three games all
So the darkness has the last word.

Generations

Old Mrs Stassinopoulos dreams
Of the blue Mediterranean
Of dancing in tavernas
Of freshly caught fish
Of the things of her past.

Young Mrs Stassinopoulos dreams
Of late night coffee bars
Of boys on bikes
Of the Beatles
Of the things of her past.

Ulie Stassinopoulos dreams
Of scoring a goal at Wembley
Of driving a fast car
Of travelling to Greece
Of the things of his future.

Early Till Late

If it's a drink you want, or a bite to eat,
Go to the shop that's down our street.
They're always open, early till late,
If you run out of cash it can go on the slate.

They've got apples and onions, biscuits and sweets,
Breadfruits and guavas, bananas and leeks,
Toothpaste and brushes, soap and shampoo,
Cat food and dog food and budgie seed too.

If it's a book you want you're in the right place,
Crime and thrillers, monsters in space,
Hospital romance, the classics as well,
All recommended by Mr Patel.

There are magazines to suit all sorts,
On fashion, computers and forty-five sports,
On gardening, knitting, huge motorbikes,
There's one there for you, whatever your likes.

All in all, whatever you need,
Mr Patel is sure to succeed,
He's just down our street and open till late,
If you run out of cash it can go on the slate.

Visit to the Dentist

When Ulie woke up
He had the toothache.
    AARGH!
'Too many sweets!' said his mam.
'Never cleans 'em!' said his gran.
'Listen who's talking!' said U.

When Ulie went to school
He still had the toothache.
    EEEGH!
'Ulie's making noises!' said Jason.
'Ulie's pulling faces!' said Alice.
'So would *you*!' said U.

When Ulie got back home
He was trying not to cry.
    O-O-OH!
'To the dentist!' said his mam.
'Told you so!' said his gran.
'Oh, leave off!' said U.

When Ulie sat in the chair
He felt the dentist's probe.
    GARRGH!
'Do sit still!' said the nurse.
'This won't hurt!' said the dentist.
'Who're you kidding?' said U.

When Ulie saw the drill
He bit the dentist's hand.
    SCREECH!

'You need a smack!' said the nurse.
'Your teeth will rot!' said the dentist.
'I don't care!' said U.

When Ulie felt the needle
He suddenly went numb.
     AH-HUM!
'Open wide!' said the dentist.
'All over now!' said the nurse.
'Nothing to it!' said U.

Classics

Ulysses and Jason
Were going to the game
Wrapped in scarves and woollen hats,
The colours all the same.
The top of the bus was empty,
They were the only two.
'My name's better'n yours,' said Jason.
'No it ain't,' said U.

'Jason was a hero,'
Said Jason, picking his ear.
'He went off to find the fleece
With the help of his girl-friend, Medea.
His ship was called the Argo
The Argonauts were her crew.
My name's better'n yours,' said Jason.
'No it ain't,' said U.

'Ulysses was the geezer,'
Said Ulie. 'Here are the facts.
He beat the Cyclops and tricked the Sirens
By stuffing his ears full of wax.
Homer wrote a book on 'im,
We've got it in the loo.'
'My name's better'n yours,' said Jason.
'No it ain't,' said U.

Jon's Juggling

On winter nights,
Most Tuesdays and Thursdays,
There's classes in
The school.
Jon Joins is learning to juggle.

There's model-making
And painting and pottery
And clog dancing
For men.
But Jon Joins is trying to juggle.

Mrs Jones
Is making a dress
And Mr Doe's carving
In wood.
But Jon Joins is determined to juggle.

They think Jon Joins
Is round the bend
And acting like
A fool.
But Jon Joins wants to juggle.

Next term, he says,
He'll try his hand
At Basic French
Instead.
But this term . . . he'll just JUGGLE!

Late for School

Peter's dad's an engine driver
He drives his train both far and wide
Through towns and fields, and back again,
Back past his house on the busy street
That leads to our school.

Some days
When he's on his early shift
He drives his train along the line
That runs across the high-arched bridge
That towers above the busy street
That leads to our school.

Some days
When he isn't too busy to think
He leans himself right out of his cab
And waves his arm to his lad, Pete,
Dawdling along the busy street
That leads to our school.

And some days
When Peter's lain too long in bed
And lost his socks, and made Mum cross,
He wishes *he* were on that train
Rushing away from the busy street
That leads to our school.

Summer Playground

On a summer's day
In high summer's heat
The children trail out
To the playground
For break.

At the edge of the grass
A giggle of girls
Turn up their faces
Like flowers seeking
The sun.

They laugh at the boys,
Too hot to play,
Too hot to fight.
They mop their brows
And wilt.

But their teacher frets
In the city street,
Longs to be with his love, his dove,
Dabbling his feet in
The summer sea.

School Visit to the Sculpture Park

'Don't touch! Don't touch!' the grown-ups glare.
'Don't tear the place apart.
Show some respect for the treasures here,
Don't you know it's ART?'

> But
> The children touch
> And feel
> And stroke
> And probe
> And explore it all.

The ballet dancer's skirt of bronze
The baby's marble cheek
The sheep's rough woollen coat of stone
The boy's lean back of teak

> The children touch
> And feel
> And stroke
> And probe
> And find it beautiful.

The teacher smiles, looks proudly round,
Explains it to the crowd.
'Permission to touch – that's what we've got,
For us, it *is* allowed!'

Choir Practice

'Greensleeves was all my joy,
And Greensleeves wa-a-s . . .'
The children are singing.
Their voices float fresh and pure
In the classroom air.
'. . . and none but my La-a-a-dy Greensleeves.'

Suddenly, in a silence,
    'SPLA-A-A-RT!'
The noise splatters through
The quiet class.
The children gasp.

The teacher jumps up from the piano,
Dashes across the room,
Stands tall, tiptoe with rage
In front of the cringeing choir.
'Whoever did Something Disgusting,
Step forward at once,' he rasps.
All is hushed. Nobody moves.
'Whoever made that Awful Noise,
Step forward right now,' he barks.
Then slowly, fearfully, little Jenny Wilde
Shuffles out to the front.

The teacher glares. 'What have you to say?'
'It was the wind,' she whispers.
The children dare to giggle, eyes wide
As they watch their teacher's face turn purple.
'Oh, very *good*,' mews the teacher. 'Thank *you*,
  Jenny Wilde.

I knew it was wind, you silly little girl,
And I want you to promise me this –
That you will never, ever,
Do that in class again.'

Little Jenny is silent,
Considers the state of her insides,
Sadly shakes her head.
'Promise me,' the teacher shouts,
'Or you shall never sing
In my choir again.'

But Jenny can't.
So Jenny never will.

Word Picture of Peter Tompkins

The
teacher
said, 'Today
I want you
to draw
me
a lovely picture
of   yourself. It will   be
a   "self-portrait".   If
it   is good I will put   it
on   the wall so I want   to
see   your very best.   OK?'
'I   can't find   a
mirror,' said Peter,
so he looked at
his shadow on the
floor, then he drew
a line   round it
with a   piece of
chalk.   Then he
filled   it with
words.   'This is
a "word   picture"
of Peter,'   he said.

Extra Work

Alice said he couldn't
And Adam said he wouldn't
And Ulie said he shouldn't . . .
But Jason DID.
He let his mouse run free
On the classroom floor.

You've never heard such nattering
                        such clattering
                        and shattering
As when that mouse ran free
On the classroom floor.

Teacher said he couldn't
Teacher said he wouldn't
Teacher said he shouldn't . . .
But teacher DID.
He gave Jason EXTRA WORK
For one whole week.

You've never heard such 'But Sir!'-ing
                        such 'Not fair!'-ing
                        and 'Have a heart!'-ing
As when he gave him EXTRA WORK
For one whole week.

Tom and the Goldfish

Jimmy Slater bullied me
And Brian Wilkins laughed at me
But when I was teased
Or lonely
Or sad
I would go down to the bike sheds
Past the gym
And into the prefab
That housed the aquarium.

I would sit
Amid the flashing brilliance of the guppies,
Under the wise watchful eyes of ancient terrapins,
But I would watch the goldfish
Humble and beautiful
Simple and majestic
As it glided through its
Tangled weeds and greenish stones
As unaware as I was
Of the laughing eyes
Watching me
Watching the fish.

Until one day
Feeling low
I came to watch
But found instead
Smashed glass and
A trickle of water from
The bench to the floor.
And there,
Surrounded by the broken shards,
Limp weed trailing over its fin,
Lay the goldfish,
Dazzling in the harsh light.

Winter Playground

In the cold winter sunshine
The children stand against the wall.
They look like washing on a line,

Neat red coat, stripy mitts,
Narrow green tights with a hole in the knee.
Still and stiff, frozen in a row.

Across the playground
Three boys are chasing a ball.
A little dog barks through the fence.

A skipping rope curves –
'One I love, two I loathe . . .' –
As the girls hop and jump.

The teacher stalks, eyes darting,
Scattering marbles in his way,
Keeping a look-out for TROUBLE.

But from the train window
It's the still ones I see, the quiet ones,
Straight and stiff against the wall,
Like washing, frozen on the line.

International Friendship Day

On International Friendship Day
Everyone in the school was given a balloon
And we all went off the park.
'Quiet please!'
Said the teacher to Jimmy Slater
Who was trying to break the sound barrier.

'Today is International Friendship Day
So all your balloons contain
A message of goodwill
To the finder.'

And on the count of three
We all let go
And our balloons drifted
Like a swarm of brightly coloured bees
Into the grey of the sky –

Apart from Alice's
Which had burst under Jimmy Slater's shoe.

'I saw that, Jimmy,' said the teacher.
'Come and see me after school and
I'll give you some extra work to do.'

'But, sir,' said Jimmy,
'It's International Friendship Day!'